Kitchen Chemistry
A Book of Science Experiments

You can become a scientist in your own kitchen. The kitchen can become your laboratory. Many items on your kitchen shelves can be used to do science experiments. Many cooking tools can be your science instruments. Grab an apron, collect your materials, and begin exploring!

Parents: Most of the experiments in this book can be done by your child alone. A few require a knife or heat source. The directions for these experiments tell your child to come to you for help. Read through the experiments and remove any you feel are inappropriate for your child at this time.

Getting Ready

1. Get permission from your parents to do the experiment.

2. Read the experiment to see what you will be doing.

3. Collect the materials you need.

Safety Tips

1. Don't mix substances unless the experiment tells you to. Some things are harmful when mixed together.

2. Don't eat or drink any substance unless the experiment tells you to.

3. Like a chemistry lab, a kitchen can be a dangerous place if you are careless. Follow directions carefully.

4. Get an adult to help you if the experiment uses a stove, hot water, or a knife.

5. If you don't understand what a word or direction means, ask an adult.

EMC 4113

Doing the Experiment

1. Read all of the directions before you start.

2. Decide what you think will happen. Mark your answer.

3. Follow the experiment steps carefully. Watch what happens.

4. Write down what you saw happening. Draw a picture of the experiment.

5. Clean Up! Always clean up your work area and put everything away.

Turn the book upside down to read about why the experiment worked the way it did. Ask an adult for help if you can't read the words yourself.

Oil and Water

Question

What will happen if you add water to oil?

You will need

- a clear drinking glass

- a spoon

- water

- vegetable oil

I think this will happen

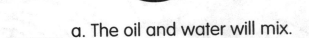

_____ a. The oil and water will mix.

_____ b. The water will float on the oil.

_____ c. The mixture will begin to fizz.

_____ d. The oil will float on the water.

EMC 4113

Follow these steps

1. Fill the glass half full of oil.

2. Carefully spoon water into the oil. You will need to put in 10 or more spoonfuls of water.

3. Watch what happens to the drops of water.

This happened:

_____

_____

_____

_____

_____

It looked like:

Raisin Fun

Question

What will happen to raisins when they are added to a soft drink (carbonated water)?

You will need

- clear drinking glass

- 10 raisins

- a soft drink
  (7-Up®, Sprite®, or club soda)

I think this will happen

_____ a. The raisins will melt.

_____ b. The raisins will explode.

_____ c. The raisins will move up and down.

_____ d. The raisins will float on top.

EMC 4113

Follow these steps

1. Pour the soda into the glass.

2. Drop the raisins into the soda.

3. Watch what happens.
   Be patient. It may take a minute.

This happened:

_____

_____

_____

_____

_____

_____

It looked like:

Explanation:
Raisins are denser (heavier) than the water, so they sink. The soft drink contains bubbles of carbon dioxide gas. The carbon dioxide bubbles are less dense than water. The bubbles collect on the raisins, causing them to float. When they reach the surface the bubbles burst and the raisins sink to the bottom again. More bubbles form and they "dance" again.

Penny Magic

Question

What will happen to dull pennies if they are washed in salt and vinegar?

You will need

- salt
- white vinegar
- dull copper pennies
- measuring spoons
- jar
- water
- paper towels

I think this will happen

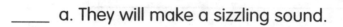

_____ a. They will make a sizzling sound.

_____ b. Nothing will happen.

_____ c. They will begin to hop up and down.

_____ d. They will become shiny.

EMC 4113

Follow these steps

1. Put two pennies on the table. Put a little salt on one penny. Put a little vinegar on the other penny. See what happens.

2. Now mix 6 tablespoons (90 ml) of vinegar and 2 tablespoons (25 gm) of salt in a jar.

3. Put the dull pennies in the jar. Stir them around for a few minutes.

4. Rinse the pennies in water and dry them with a towel.

This happened:

_____

_____

_____

_____

_____

It looked like:

Explanation:
The dull film on the pennies forms when oxygen from the air mixes with copper in the pennies. When vinegar and table salt are mixed together they make hydrochloric acid. The acid mixture breaks down the film on the pennies, leaving them shining like new.

Mix It Up

Question

What happens when vinegar and baking soda are mixed?

You will need

- soda bottle
- balloon
- baking soda
- vinegar
- funnel
- a large spoon
- paper towels (for clean-up)

I think this will happen

____ a. Nothing will happen.

____ b. A loud explosion will happen.

____ c. A gas will be made.

____ d. The vinegar will turn pink.

EMC 4113

Follow these steps

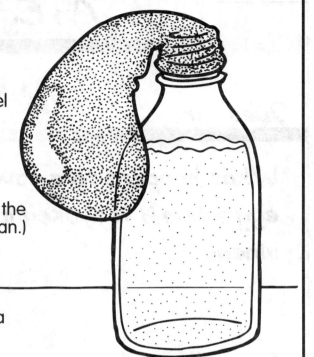

1. Use the funnel to help you put 2 spoonfuls of baking soda in a balloon. Clean the funnel before the next step.

2. Use the funnel to help you put 8 spoonfuls of vinegar in the bottle.

3. Carefully stretch the end of the balloon over the top of the bottle. (Do this as quickly as you can.)

4. Tip the baking soda out of the balloon into the bottle.

5. Watch what happens when the baking soda and the vinegar mix.

This happened:

_____

_____

_____

_____

_____

It looked like:

Explanation:
When you mix two substances, the molecules react with each other. Sometimes the molecules attract each other and bond together. This creates a new substance. When vinegar and baking soda are mixed they bond together to produce the gas carbon dioxide.

An Egg Mystery

Question

What happens to a raw egg when it is soaked in vinegar?

You will need

- a raw egg (in its shell)

- a clear drinking glass

- vinegar

I think this will happen

_____ a. It will become rubbery.

_____ b. It will cook inside.

_____ c. The yolk will disappear.

_____ d. It will change color.

EMC 4113

Follow these steps

1. Put the raw egg in a glass.

2. Fill the glass with enough vinegar to cover the egg.

3. Let the egg sit in the vinegar for two days.

4. Take the egg out of the glass and see what has happened.

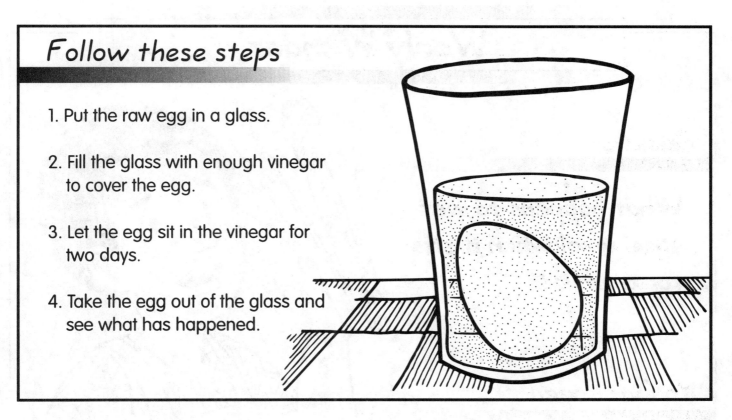

This happened:

It looked like:

_____

_____

_____

_____

_____

_____

Explanation:
Vinegar, which is an acid, will cause the calcium in the egg shell to dissolve. The egg will appear to be rubbery in texture.

Wooly Wonder

Question

What happens to wet steel wool when it sits for a while?

You will need

- steel wool
- water
- cup of vinegar

- dish
- tongs

Parents: You can purchase steel wool at a hardware store or in most supermarkets.

I think this will happen

_____ a. The steel wool will stay wet.

_____ b. The steel wool will start to disappear.

_____ c. The steel wool will start to turn orangy-red.

_____ d. The steel wool will start to grow.

EMC 4113

Follow these steps

1. Hold the steel wool with tongs and put it in the vinegar. Let it sit for 30 minutes.

2. Take the steel wool out of the vinegar. Put it on the dish.

3. Add a few drops of water to the dish.

4. Let the steel wool sit for a day. See what happens.

This happened:

_____

_____

_____

_____

_____

_____

It looked like:

Explanation:
The orangy-red color is rust. The vinegar removes the protective coating from the steel wool so it will rust. The drops of water make it rust even faster.

Shake It Up

Question

What happens to cream when it is shaken for a while?

You will need

- a jar with a lid
- whipping cream

I think this will happen

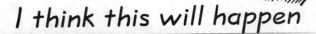

_____ a. The cream will turn sour.

_____ b. The cream will turn to butter.

_____ c. The cream will get hot.

_____ d. Nothing will happen.

16

Follow these steps

1. Fill the jar half full of cream.

2. Put the lid on the jar. Be sure it is on tight.

3. Shake the jar as you count to 100.
   Look at the cream. Do you see a change?

4. Shake the jar and count to 100 again.
   Look to see if there is a change.

5. Keep shaking and counting until you
   see a lump in the cream. Taste a lump.
   What have you made?

This happened:

_____

_____

_____

_____

_____

_____

It looked like:

Explanation:
The yellow lump is butter. Rinse the remaining milk from the butter and spread it on toast or crackers for a snack.
Cream consists of butterfat suspended in water. When you shake the cream, you force the fat drops to separate
from the water and come together. This is called coalescing.

Is It Fat?

What happens when you rub water and butter on a sheet of brown paper?

You will need

- a brown paper bag

- water

- small amount of butter

- spoon

I think this will happen

_____ a. Both spots will dry.

_____ b. Both spots will leave a spot.

_____ c. Water will dry and butter will leave a spot.

_____ d. Butter will dry and water will leave a spot.

EMC 4113

Follow these steps

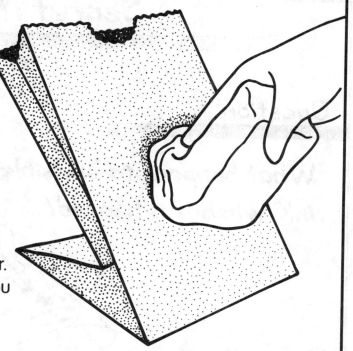

1. Rub a little butter on the brown paper bag.

2. Put a few drops of water on another part of the bag.

3. Let the bag sit for an hour.

4. Look at the place you rubbed the butter. What do you see? Look at the place you dropped the water. What do you see? Which one left a shiny spot?

This happened:

It looked like:

_____

_____

_____

_____

_____

_____

Explanation:
Both water and butter will leave a translucent spot on the bag when they are wet. The water spot will disappear when the water dries. The butter spot will not disappear because of the oil left by the fat. Find other items in your refrigerator you think contain fat. Rub them on the brown paper and see if they leave a greasy spot.

Secret Messages

Question

What happens to "invisible ink" when it is heated?

You will need

- oven mitts
- a lamp
- lemon juice
- white writing paper
- cotton swab or thin paintbrush

I think this will happen

_____ a. My message will stay a mystery.

_____ b. My message will appear on the paper.

_____ c. My message will burn up.

_____ d. My message will disappear forever.

Parents: This experiment involves using the heat of a light bulb. You will need to help your child with that step.

EMC 4113

Follow these steps

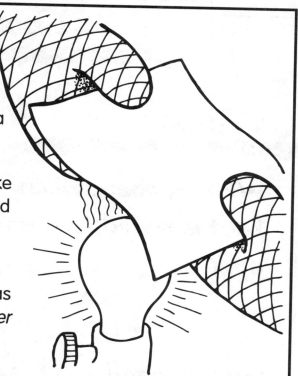

1. Write a secret message on the paper using lemon juice for ink. Use a thin paintbrush or a cotton swab to write your message. Let it dry.

2. Ask your parent to help you with this part. Take the shade off of a lamp. Turn the lamp on and let the bulb get hot.

3. Put on the oven mitts and hold your message close to the light bulb. Watch what happens as the paper begins to get hot. (*Don't let the paper touch the light bulb. You don't want it to catch fire.*)

This happened:

_____

_____

_____

_____

_____

It looked like:

Explanation:
Heat caused a chemical change to the "invisible ink." The paper that soaked up the lemon juice turns brown at a lower temperature than the rest of the paper. This lets the message mysteriously appear.

Cooking Eggs

Question

What happens when heat is added to a raw egg?

You will need

- water
- small saucepan
- 2 raw eggs
- 2 saucers
- stove

I think this will happen

_____ a. The egg will stay the same.

_____ b. The egg will become solid.

_____ c. A baby chick will come out of the egg.

_____ d. The egg will turn brown.

Parents: This experiment requires the use of a stove. You will need to help your child with that step.

EMC 4113

Follow these steps

1. Crack one raw egg and put it in a saucer. Look at the liquid parts.

2. Carefully put the other egg in a pan. Fill the pan with enough water to cover the egg.

3. Ask your parents for help with this step. Have your parent put the pan on the stove and turn on the fire. Let the egg cook until it has boiled for five minutes.

4. Have your parent take the egg out of the hot water and sit it on a saucer to cool. When the egg is cool, take off the shell.

5. What happened to the liquid part of the egg when it was cooked?

This happened:

_____

_____

_____

_____

_____

_____

It looked like:

Explanation:
Eggs are made of proteins, fats, and water. The water in a raw egg flows between the proteins. When the egg is heated, all the molecules inside begin to move rapidly. This movement causes the water in the egg white and the yolk to get trapped in the proteins. It can't move around any more. This makes the egg become hard.

Floating Eggs

Question

Which solutions will make the egg float? ??

You will need

- 4 raw eggs
- water
- cornstarch
- vinegar
- salt

- food color
- 4 clear drinking glasses
- tablespoon spoon
- black crayon

I think this will happen

____ a. An egg will float in food color and water.

____ b. An egg will float in cornstarch and water.

____ c. An egg will float in salt and water.

____ d. An egg will float in vinegar and water.

EMC 4113

Follow these steps

1. Number the glasses 1, 2, 3, and 4.

2. Fill each glass 2/3 full of water.

3. Stir one of these in each glass:
   - Glass 1 - a few drops of food coloring
   - Glass 2 - two large spoonfuls of cornstarch
   - Glass 3 - two large spoonfuls of salt
   - Glass 4 - two large spoonfuls of vinegar

4. Carefully put one egg in each glass. Watch to see which eggs float.

This happened:

_____

_____

_____

_____

_____

It looked like:

Explanation:

An uncooked egg is heavier (more dense) than plain water, so it will not float. It is also heavier than water with cornstarch or vinegar. The egg is not as dense as salt water so it will float. If you have trouble getting your egg to float, add more salt.

Soap Surprise

Question

What will happen when soap is added to a bowl of water and food coloring?

You will need

- cereal bowl

- water

- food color

- liquid detergent

I think this will happen

_____ a. The water will turn white.

_____ b. The soap will make bubbles.

_____ c. The food color will move in the bowl.

_____ d. The water will begin to make noises.

EMC 4113

Follow these steps

1. Put about an inch (2.5 cm) of water in the bowl. Let the water sit until it is still.

2. Very carefully drop a few spots of food color into the bowl.

3. Slowly pour some detergent down the side of the bowl into the water. Watch what happens.

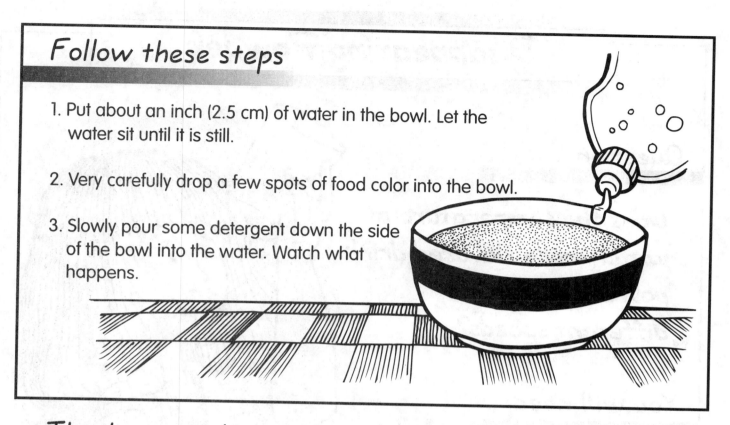

This happened:

_____

_____

_____

_____

_____

It looked like:

Disappearing Powder

Question

Does the temperature of water make flavored drink powder dissolve at different speeds?

You will need

- powdered drink mix
- 3 clear drinking glasses
- boiling water
- ice water
- water at room temperature (Fill a glass with water and let it sit one hour.)

I think this will happen

_____ a. There will be no difference.

_____ b. The ice water will be fastest.

_____ c. The room temperature water will be fastest.

_____ d. The boiling water will be fastest.

Parents: You will need to help your child with this experiment since it uses boiling water.

EMC 4113

Follow these steps

1. Ask your parents to fill one glass half full of boiling water. You fill the other two glasses half full. Put ice water in one cup. Put room temperature water in the other cup.

2. Drop a pinch of drink mix into each of the glasses. Watch what happens.

This happened:

_____

_____

_____

_____

_____

_____

It looked like:

Red or Green?

Question

What happens when you mix a substance with "indicator liquid"?

You will need

- indicator liquid
- eyedropper
- 6 clear plastic cups
- water

- a little bit of:
  soapy water
  lemon juice
  milk
  soda water
  orange juice
  vinegar

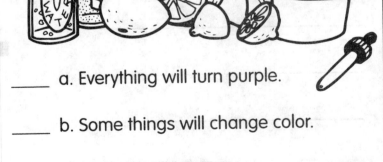

I think this will happen

____ a. Everything will turn purple.

____ b. Some things will change color.

____ c. Nothing will happen.

____ d. Everything will begin to bubble.

Parents: You will need to help your child make the indicator liquid for this experiment. The directions are on page 32.

EMC 4113

Follow these steps

1. Put a little indicator liquid in each cup.

2. Use the eyedropper to add a few drops of each of these to a different cup. Wash the eyedropper in water before you fill it each time.

- milk
- lemon juice
- orange juice
- soapy water
- soda water
- vinegar

3. Watch what happens.

This happened:

It looked like:

The milk_____

The lemon juice_____

The orange juice_____

The soapy water_____

The soda water_____

The vinegar_____

Parents: You will need to help your child prepare this liquid to use with the experiment on page 31. Let your child help as much as possible.

Indicator Liquid

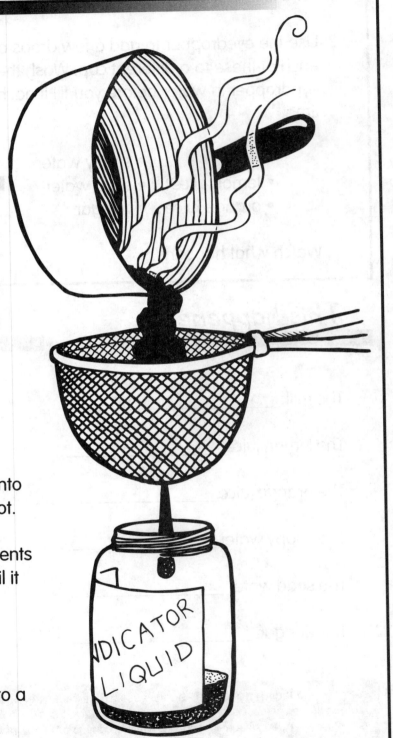

You will need

- half a red cabbage
- pot
- water
- sieve or strainer
- jar

Follow these steps

1. Shred or tear half a red cabbage into small pieces. Put the pieces in a pot.

2. Add a cup of water. Ask your parents to put the pot on the stove and boil it for fifteen minutes.

3. Let the cabbage cool.

4. Pour the liquid through a sieve into a jar.

EMC 4113